"Let go of your mind & then be mindful."

RUMI

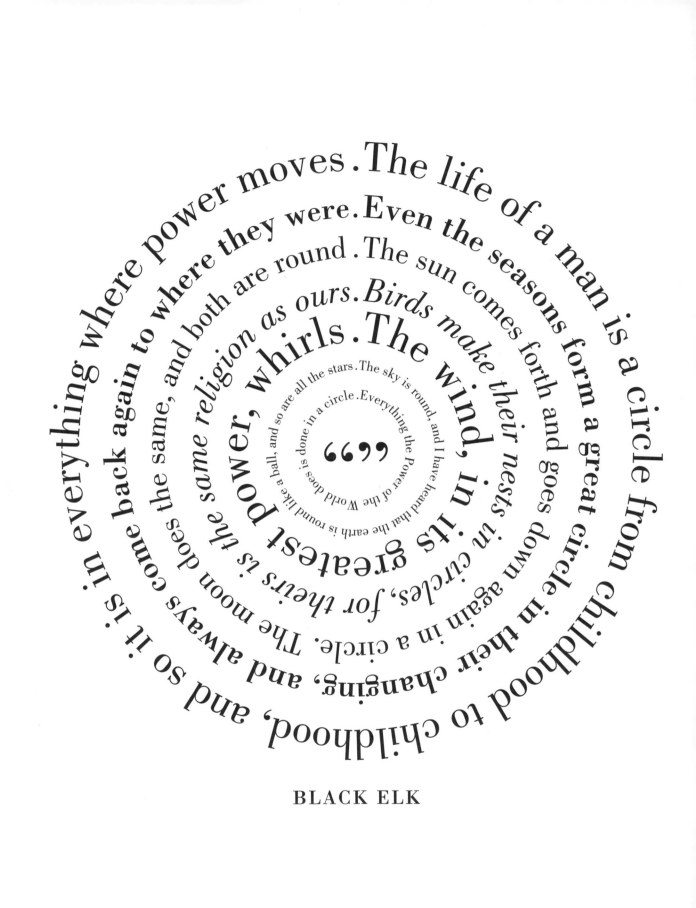

The life of a man is a circle from childhood to childhood, and so it is in everything where power moves. The sun comes forth and goes down again in a circle. The moon does the same, and both are round. Even the seasons form a great circle in their changing, and always come back again to where they were. The wind, in its greatest power, whirls. Birds make their nests in circles, for theirs is the same religion as ours. The sky is round, and I have heard that the earth is round like a ball, and so are all the stars. Everything the Power of the World does is done in a circle.

66 99

BLACK ELK

A Mindfulness
Colouring Book

COLOUR
yourself
CALM

Written & compiled by
Tiddy Rowan

Mandalas by
Paul Heussenstamm

Quadrille
PUBLISHING

Peace of the Soul

Day After Night

Dance of the Butterfly

Light of Heaven

Moon Goddess

Copper Circle

Pathfinder

Fruit of the Soul

Ocean Rainbow

Indian Colours

Tibetan Sun

Chartres Hologram

Sun within the Sea

Nature's Kitchen

Black Crown

Ancient Future

Force Behind the Wolf

Sri Yantra

Red Snake Dream

Lotus with Eyes

Eternal Living Flame

Indian Flower

Firing Love Bloom

Feather Mandala

Rainbow Ananda

Black African Flower

Man in a Maze

Full Rainbow of Being

Out of Hands

Chakra Wheel

Electric Hearts

Happiness of the Soul

Inner Peace

About the quotes

About the illustrator & author

INTRODUCTION

Colour Yourself Calm is a mindfulness-inspired colouring book including 33 original colour mandalas with their accompanying black-and-white templates to colour in. Inspirational quotes and mindfulness techniques accompany each image to enhance the experience. Mandalas are designs that draw your eye towards their centres, and in doing so, focus the mind. Colouring in mandalas relaxes the mind, body and spirit, relieves stress and is a chance to explore your own inner creativity.

Historically, mandalas are ancient forms of meditative art: the symmetrical, concentric circles are designed to ease the overloaded mind and release its deep-rooted creative and expressive inclination. By becoming absorbed in colouring in an object of beauty, the reader will embark on a practical exercise in mindfulness. This is an easy way to relax the mind, body and spirit, whilst subconsciously developing self knowledge, expanding the imagination and creating a sense of wellbeing.

The first mandalas were almost certainly created as far back as the fourth century by Buddhist monks as an art form on which to meditate. Mandalas are found in deeply rooted and diverse cultures and religions across the world, wherever there is an impulse to tap into an unexplored part of the mind or spirit.

Psychologists (pioneered by Carl Jung) have observed that people with no grounding in Eastern mysticism draw mandala-like shapes spontaneously in psychotherapy. Such drawings are thought to represent an attempt by the conscious self to recognise and integrate unconscious knowledge. A mandala, in this light, reflects the inner expression of the person creating it — tapping into the subconscious and connecting to a deeper part of the psyche or soul that is not easily expressed in the language of words.

So, relax, unwind and explore your inner subconscious by colouring yourself calm!

Kurukuli Mandala
TIBET, NINETEENTH CENTURY

MINDFULNESS:

PRACTICE

Practising a simple mindfulness exercise before getting started helps to centre your attention. Sit in a comfortable but upright position, drop your shoulders, and follow each breath for a few moments.

Turn your attention to whichever mandala attracts you the most. Let your conscious mind follow the imagery, circles and cycles until you reach the centre of the mandala. Become aware of the colours and immerse yourself in the imagery.

The objective is to empty your chattering mind and focus on the images in the mandala. If your attention wanders – focus once again on your breathing and return to the image. Use the centre of the mandala as your anchor to return to when you feel your concentration wandering.

Gradually, shift your focus to the mandala template on the right-hand side of the page and start to colour it in. You can follow the colours in the picture or you can choose your own colours at random, selecting those that appeal to you for any given section.

As you colour in, keep your attention on the activity, parking your mind into neutral so you can access your subconscious. Areas of your deeper self are then able to come to the surface and communicate with your conscious mind.

This also gives your right brain (emotional, instinctive and imaginative) a chance to interact with your left brain (logic and reasoning) so they can disentangle problems and re-create a sense of balance. See it as a way of letting your instincts become apparent.

There is no right or wrong way to access the mandalas. Just the action of looking and staying within their framework is an exercise in practical mindfulness. These guidelines are simply to help you find your own individual response.

The three key ingredients to being mindful are time, patience and attentiveness. So stop, sit, be still and look mindfully into a mandala, begin colouring and let your inner adventure begin...

EXERCISE

The essence of the discipline is in the word – mindfulness – being mindful – and not "mind full". Use your breathing as an anchor and access point to the state of being mindful and it will strengthen your mind by keeping it focused.

It's easy to read a few words on the importance of your breathing or the value of being mindful of what you say to others, not dwelling on things you cannot change or future events that may not happen. But practising it, actually connecting to mindfulness, takes commitment to begin. All the benefits will become apparent as soon as you decide to engage with it. And like everything – it gets better with practice. Eventually, it will empower and encourage you to take more and more steps, until you become mindful in all the activities in your life.

The mandalas in this book will reinforce the importance of staying in (or returning to) the here and now. Selecting a mandala to colour in and keeping your mind focused on a single thought – or simply the activity itself – is an exercise in mindfulness.

As you develop this practice, it becomes easier to apply mindfulness in other areas, to pay more attention to everyday activities and to focus on your breathing whenever you need to reach for a moment of calm.

BREATHING

A deeply relaxed person breathes around seven times a minute. Slow your breathing down and you will automatically relax. This is helpful when you need to focus before an important interview or presentation, during periods of stress or simply to keep calm.

Breathe in (count to five – approximately)

Hold it (count to two)

Breathe out slowly (count to five – approximately)

Repeat, a couple of times then allow your breathing to find its own slower rhythm without forcing it.

Peace of the Soul

Be mindful – not mind full.

Day After Night

"Who looks outside, dreams; who looks inside, awakes."
CARL JUNG

Dance of the Butterfly

Live in the present moment.
Only be aware of what is happening right now.

Light of Heaven

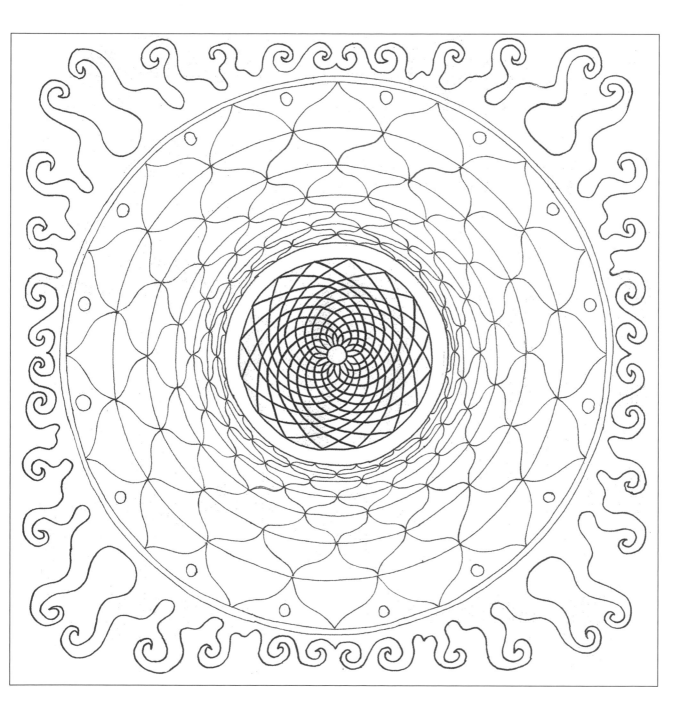

"My religion is very simple. My religion is kindness."
DALAI LAMA

Moon Goddess

The centre doesn't have to be "out there".
It can be the centre of your mind or your self.

Copper Circle

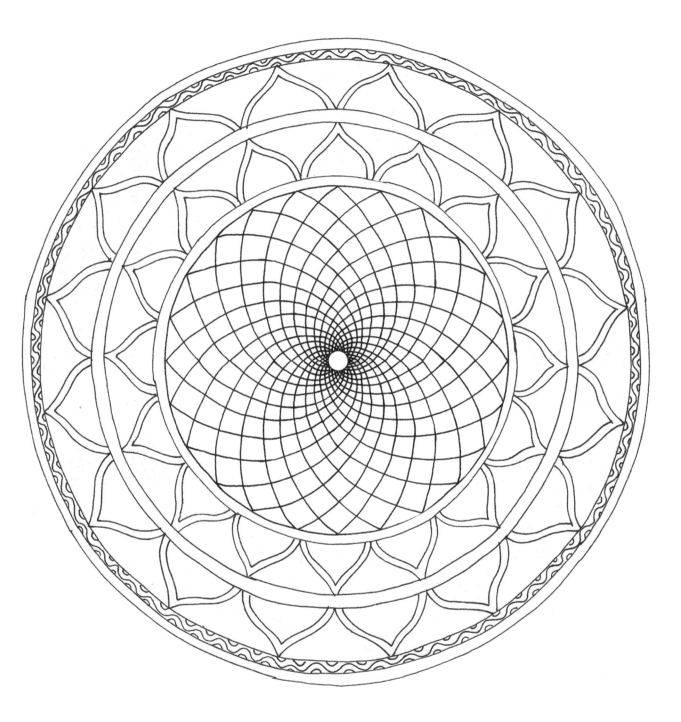

By concentrating on colouring in, worries of
the past and anxieties about the future dissipate.

Pathfinder

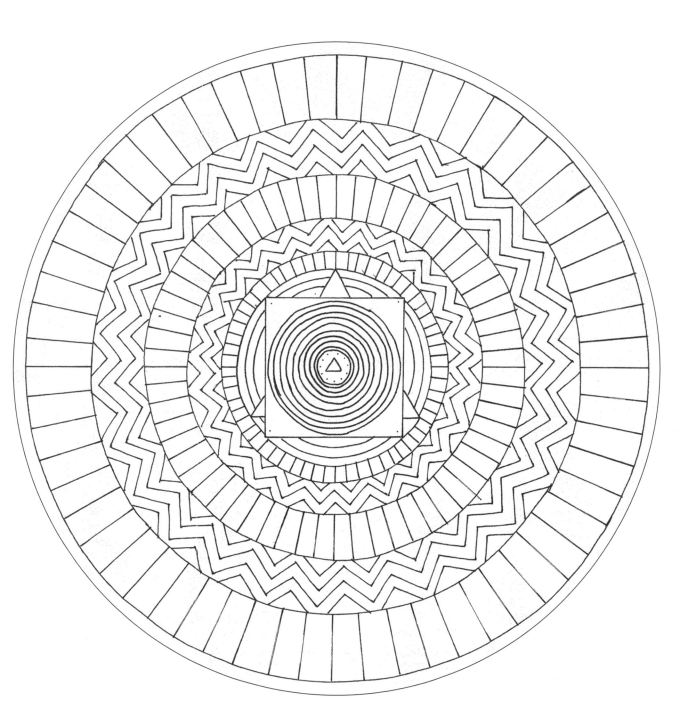

"A person who never made a mistake never tried anything new."
ALBERT EINSTEIN

Fruit of the Soul

"Happiness resides not in possessions, and not in gold,
happiness dwells in the soul."
DEMOCRITUS

Ocean Rainbow

The spectrum of colours reflects positive energy.

Indian Colours

Be mindful of feeling centred.

Tibetan Sun

"The secret of health for both mind and body is...
to live in the present moment wisely and earnestly."
BUDDHA

Chartres Hologram

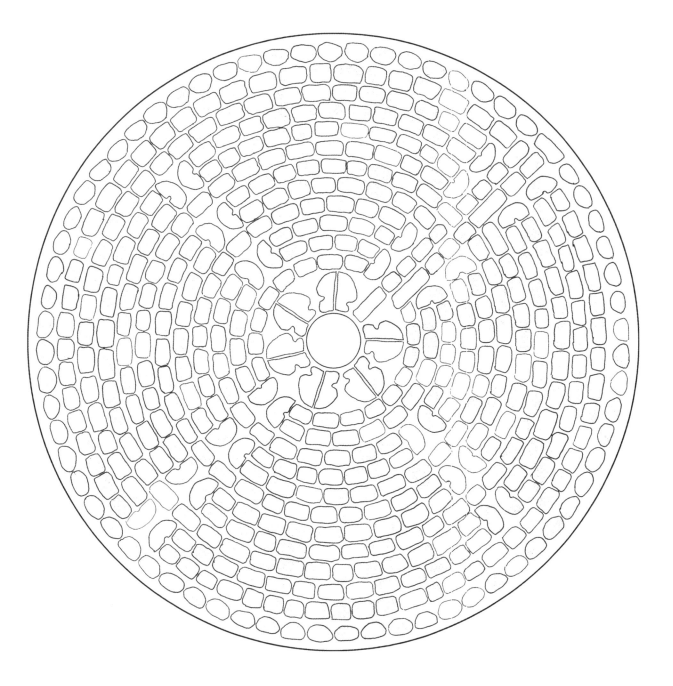

View the world with a positive outlook and
the reflections cast upon you will be beautiful.

Sun within the Sea

*"Chance is always powerful. Let your hook be always cast;
in the pool where you least expect it, there will be a fish."*
OVID

Nature's Kitchen

Let the natural healing process revive
and restore your mind and body.

Black Crown

Focus on the inner dot. Allow your mind's eye to create different patterns and illusions, which will centre you and give you a feeling of calm.

Ancient Future

*"What lies behind us and what lies before us are
tiny matters compared to what lies within us."*
RALPH WALDO EMERSON

Force Behind the Wolf

Let your imagination roam free.

Sri Yantra

Be mindful of the powerful energy within you.

Red Snake Dream

"Sometimes dreams are wiser than waking."
BLACK ELK

Lotus with Eyes

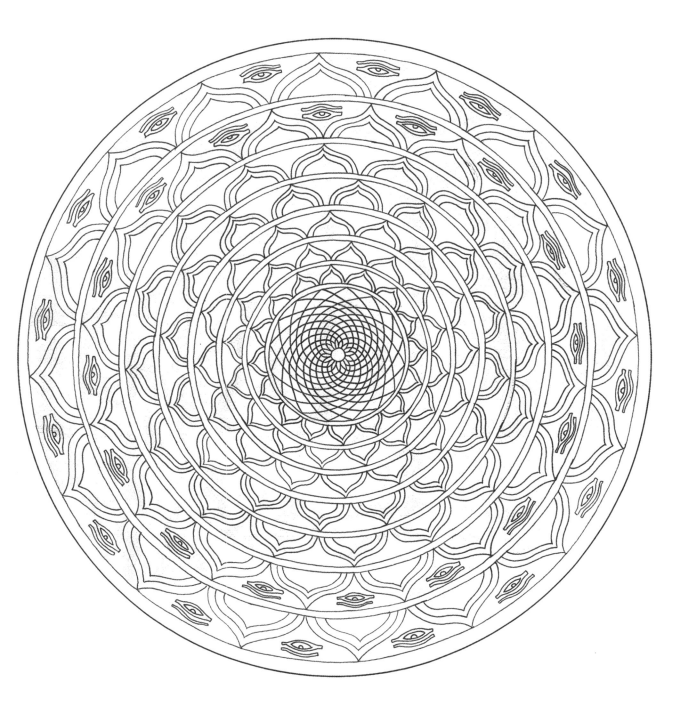

There are more ways of seeing than just looking straight ahead.

Eternal Living Flame

Be mindful, as you colour, of drawing energy in from the sun.

Indian Flower

Focus on a particular problem. Gradually, untie those
knots as you colour towards the centre of this mandala.

Firing Love Bloom

"I found I could say things with colour and shapes that I couldn't say any other way – things I had no words for."
GEORGIA O'KEEFFE

Feather Mandala

"Let your life lightly dance on the edges of time like dew on the tip of a leaf."
RABINDRANATH TAGORE

Rainbow Ananda

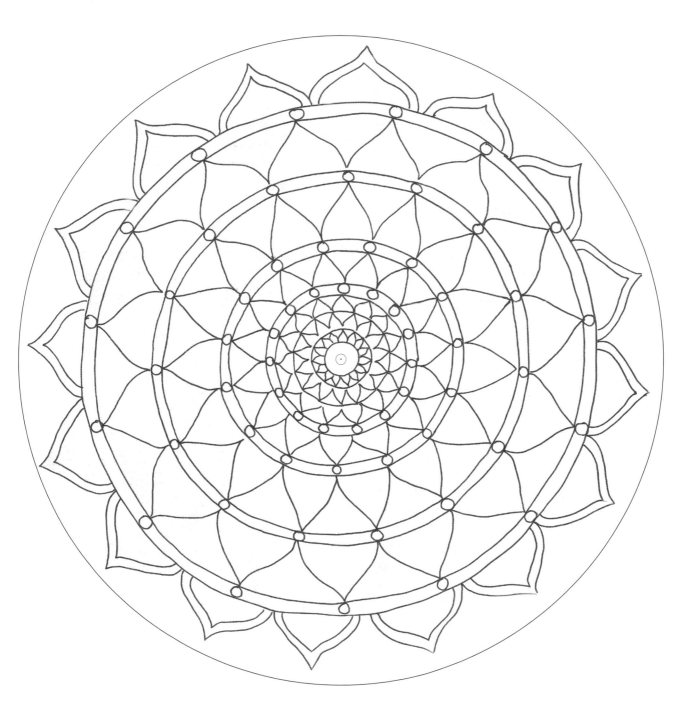

Spend a few moments soaking up the gentle
feeling of this calming mandala.

Black African Flower

Face your fears and overcome them through
the process of colouring them out.

Man in a Maze

Let your right brain and left brain meet and work together in the centre.

Full Rainbow of Being

The mind is a workshop full of busy ideas, thoughts and worries.
But deep in the centre there is a stillness, where the inner self
is protected from the mind machine. Find this centre through
colouring yourself calm.

Out of Hands

"What is a friend? A single soul dwelling in two bodies."
ARISTOTLE

Chakra Wheel

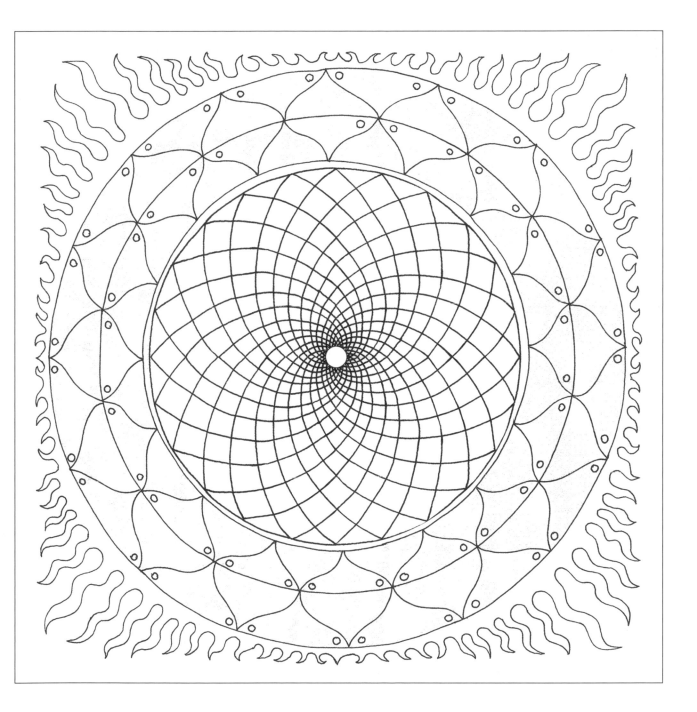

**Be mindful of the enormity of the cosmos
and our place and purpose within it.**

Electric Hearts

"Love is the only reality and it is not a mere sentiment.
It is the ultimate truth that lies at the heart of creation."
RABINDRANATH TAGORE

Happiness of the Soul

Colour in your happiness.

Inner Peace

"It isn't enough to talk about peace. One must believe in it.
And it isn't enough to believe in it. One must work at it."
ELEANOR ROOSEVELT

" A mandala is a very ancient guide that symbolically allows you to visually look into yourself. The process of colouring in a mandala can give you profound insights into your psyche and your mind. It appears simple, and it is, yet there are layers of growth and understanding and even a transforming of consciousness that are revealed in a mandala painting, whether colouring one in or simply looking at one. The truth about mandala meditating is just to sit still and gaze upon one. Once you have coloured in several mandalas – or even several parts of one mandala – you will begin to feel patterns within yourself. This is valuable because it allows you to recognise patterns and begin to communicate with your conscious self through these core patterns. "

PAUL HEUSSENSTAMM

QUOTES ARE TAKEN FROM:

ALBERT EINSTEIN was a theoretical physicist. He is renowned for developing the general theory of relativity and received the Nobel Prize for Physics in 1921.

ARISTOTLE is one of greatest philosophers from ancient Greece, his work has had a long-lasting influence on the development of all Western philosophical theories.

BLACK ELK was a famous holy man, traditional healer and visionary of the North American tribe of Oglala Lakota (Sioux).

BUDDHA is the founder and original teacher of Buddhism.

CARL JUNG was a revolutionary psychiatrist and psychotherapist. He is best known for having founded analytical psychology.

DALAI LAMA is a high lama, guru and teacher of Tibetan Buddhism.

DEMOCRITUS was known as the "laughing philosopher", who influenced modern science more than any other pre-Socratic philosopher.

ELEANOR ROOSEVELT was an American politician and the longest-serving First Lady of the United States.

GEORGIA O'KEEFFE was a twentieth-century American painter who focused on finding abstract forms in nature for seven decades.

OVID was a Roman poet whose work strongly influenced more recent European art and literature.

RALPH WALDO EMERSON was an American preacher, philosopher, lecturer and poet, and the leader of the Transcendentalist movement.

RUMI was a thirteenth-century Persian poet, theologian and Sufi mystic.

RABINDRANATH TAGORE was a Bengali poet, novelist and painter. He won the Nobel Prize in Literature in 1913, the first non-European to do so.

PAUL HEUSSENSTAMM

Paul Heussenstamm is a master painter of mandalas and other forms of spiritual paintings. He has painted and drawn over 1000 mandalas and has taught worldwide for 25 years; as well as at his studio in California, US.

Since 1996, he has worked for the Chopra Center for Wellbeing, sharing his art at almost every major event that Deepak Chopra hosts. He is the sanctuary artist at the Agape International Spiritual Centre in Culver City in California, which has 10,000 local members.

TIDDY ROWAN

Tiddy Rowan has travelled extensively in her career producing television commercials, followed by working in the art market and researching and writing books. In the 1970s she practised meditation and yoga for the first time and has been studying techniques, beliefs and related philosophies ever since. Her interest in mindfulness has led to practising it and also researching the fusion of its Western and Eastern roots.

Editorial director Anne Furniss
Creative director Helen Lewis
Editor Romilly Morgan
Designer Emily Lapworth
Production director Vincent Smith
Production controller James Finan

First published in 2014 by
Quadrille Publishing Ltd
www.quadrille.co.uk

Quadrille is an imprint of Hardie Grant
www.hardiegrant.com.au

Design & layout © 2014 Quadrille Publishing Ltd

Text on pages: 6, 8, 9, 11, 15, 19, 21, 27, 29, 33, 37, 39, 43,
45, 49, 51, 53, 59, 61, 63, 65, 69, 73 © 2014 Tiddy Rowan
Text on page: 77 © Paul Heussenstam
Mandalas designs on pages: 1, 4, 5, 10–76 © Paul Heussenstam
Kurukuli Mandala on page: 7 © John & Tsering Lhakey Dugger Collection

Reprinted in 2014 (twice), 2015 (four times)
10 9 8 7

British Library Cataloguing-in-Publication Data
A catalogue record for this book is available from the British Library.

ISBN: 978 184949 514 1

Printed in China

Publisher's note: Meditation, mindfulness and breathing exercises are beneficial for most people and
generally harmless, but those unsure of its suitability for them should consult a medical practitioner
before attempting any of the exercises in this book. Neither the publishers nor the author can accept
responsibility for any harm incurred as a result of following the guidelines in this book.